DORSET

POCKET ADDRESS BOOK

Halswood

Published by Halswood Stationers

Copyright © Halswood Stationers
Image copyright © Roger Holman

British Library Cataloguing-in-Publication Data
A CIP record for this title is available from the British Library

ISBN 978 0 85717 041 5

HALSWOOD STATIONERS
Halsgrove House,
Ryelands Industrial Estate,
Bagley Road, Wellington, Somerset TA21 9PZ
Tel: 01823 653777   Fax: 01823 216796
email: sales@halsgrove.com

Part of the Halsgrove group of companies.
Information on all Halsgrove titles is available at: www.halsgrove.com

Printed and bound in China by Toppan Leefung Printing Ltd (0)

Opening Address

Many of us still find the traditional address book so much more convenient, and ultimately more dependable than an electronic device. This one is made to fit in a pocket or handbag, having plenty of room for those vital addresses, confidential notes and reminders. It is also carefully designed to look good too. We've personalised it further by including some of the very best reminders of Dorset's beautiful landscape taken by photographer Roger Holman. So whether you have bought this mini address book for yourself, or as a gift, its owner can now carry a little bit of Dorset with them along with all their vital information.

Hengistbury.

a

a

b

Gold Hill, Shaftesbury.

b

b

Melbury Hill.

C

C

d

Poole.

d

River Stour.

Whitemill.

g

Charmouth to Lyme.

g

Fontmell poppies.

h

Kimmeridge.

Mudeford.

j

k

St Catherine's Chapel.

Rough weather, Chesil.

Eyebridge floods.

m

m

Horton Tower.

O

Osmington Mills.

0

Swyre Head.

p
q

Corfe Castle.

Golden Cap.

S

S

Surfers at Kimmeridge.

t

u

Poole.

u

Portland.

V

Fiddleford Mill.

W

x
y
z

xyz

About the photographer

Roger Holman was born in 1932 near Wimborne, not far from where he lives today, and educated at the Queen Elizabeth Grammar School. On leaving he joined the family firm, which he continued to run — apart from time spent in the RAF on National Service — until he handed it over to two of his sons. He discovered photography in his teens and has been photographing aspects of his home county ever since. He is the author of Images of the Dorset Coast, Images of Dorset County, Dorset the Glorious County, A Spirit of Weymouth and Portland and co-author of Dorset's Most beautiful Buildings.